Illustrated by Jason Beene
Layouts by Art Mawhinney

Puss In Boots ® & © 2011 DreamWorks Animation L.L.C.

Published by
Louis Weber, C.E.O., Publications International, Ltd.
7373 North Cicero Avenue, Lincolnwood, Illinois 60712

Ground Floor, 59 Gloucester Place, London W1U 8JJ

Customer Service: 1-800-595-8484 or customer_service@pilbooks.com

www.pilbooks.com

p i kids is a trademark of Publications International, Ltd.,
and is registered in the United States.

Look and Find is a trademark of Publications International, Ltd.,
and is registered in the United States and Canada.

8 7 6 5 4 3 2 1

ISBN-13: 978-1-4508-2696-9
ISBN-10: 1-4508-2696-2

DREAMWORKS
PUSS IN BOOTS®

pi kids®

publications international, ltd.

Before he was a legend, Puss In Boots lived in the San Ricardo orphanage with Humpty Alexander Dumpty. The two friends dreamed of finding the magic beans of legend. Can you find these other kinds of beans?

Jelly beans

Coffee beans

Chili beans

Lima beans

Mexican jumping beans

Green beans

It's another busy day in the San Ricardo town square! Puss becomes an instant hero by saving the Comandante's mother while Humpty looks on. Can you seek out these citizens of San Ricardo?

Accordion player

Pretty señorita

This vendor

Imelda

This vendor

Little Boy Blue

Puss In Boots and the Masked Stranger break into Jack and Jill's hotel room, looking for the magic beans. Can you search the room and see what other hotel-related things turn up?

Room key

Do Not Disturb sign

Ice bucket

Tourist's Guide to San Ricardo

Room service tray

Toiletries

They're really light on their paws at the Cat Cantina! Puss In Boots and the Masked Stranger are facing off in a Tuesday Night Dance Fight. Step inside and see if you can find the following items there.

This dish of milk

Lava lamp

Tuesday night dance fight poster

Cow portrait

Flamenco guitar player

Fish dinner

Puss and Kitty have made it inside Jack and Jill's wagon to stake their claim on the magic beans. But first, they'll have to look through all the stuff that the couple has collected. Can you find these things that belong to Jack and Jill?

Bag of pig treats for Pork Chop

Baby-name book

Jack's eye patch

Mini muffins

Shaving kit

Hotel del Toro Negro coffee cup

Humpty, Puss, and Kitty have made it to the Cloud World and are searching for the Golden Goose. Can you look through the scenery and find these rainforest plants and flowers?

Fern

Bamboo tree

Coffee plant

Orchid

Banana tree

Venus flytrap

Puss is shocked when he returns to San Ricardo and realizes that Humpty, Jack and Jill, and even Kitty were all plotting against him! See if you can find these everyday sights in the town square.

Tapas restaurant sign

Hitching post for horse

Comandante's portrait

IMELDA AVE

Imelda Avenue street sign

Statue of San Ricardo

Mariachi musician

After a frantic chase through San Ricardo, Humpty's coach crashes on the bridge. Now Puss must choose between Humpty and the Golden Goose. See if you can find things that were tossed about in the wreck!

Golden egg

Wagon wheel

Horseshoe

Chunk of bricks

Coffee pot

Cloth wing from wagon

Bean begins with the letter B. Head back to the orphanage and find a few more things that begin with B.

Black ink

Butterfly

Blanket

Bean Grower's Guide

Bench

Broom

Take another trip to the marketplace and see if you can find the following items.

Dried peppers

Red roses

Birdcage

Tray of meat pies

For Sale sign

Humpty's rock pile

Head back to Jack and Jill's hotel room and look around for these things that lock up.

Room safe

Combination lock

Jewelry box

Pig crate

Window lock

Double bolt

The local cats love all the Tuesday night action at their favorite cantina. Before the fur flies, stop by and identify these kinds of cats!

Siamese cat

Hairless cat

Manx cat

Maine Coon cat

Black cat

Orange tabby cat

With their sinister ways, Jack and Jill make quite a couple. Can you search their wagon and find some more pairs?

Pair of rubber gloves

Pair of dice

Pair of sunglasses

Pair of earrings

His and Hers bathrobes

Pair of pig slippers

It's a jungle out there! Travel back to the rain forest and see if you can find these animal shapes formed by the tangled vines.

Monkey

Snake

Frog

Chameleon

Macaw

Jaguar

It's obvious Humpty was not playing around with Puss In Boots. Can you head back to San Ricardo and find a few things that children at the orphanage do like to play with?

Hobby horse

Scooter

Soccer ball

Kite

Croquet set

Wagon

While the plume on Puss In Boots' hat stayed put, feathers were really flying near the San Ricardo Bridge. See if you can find these:

The Great Terror feather

Golden Goose feathers

Pigeon feather

Rooster feather

Peacock feather

Flamingo feather